2015

JANUARY

M	T	W	T	F	S	S
			1	2	3	4
5	6	7	8	9	10	11
12	13	14	15	16	17	18
19	20	21	22	23	24	25
26	27	28	29	30	31	

FEBRUARY

M	T	W	T	F	S	S
						1
2	3	4	5	6	7	8
9	10	11	12	13	14	15
16	17	18	19	20	21	22
23	24	25	26	27	28	

MARCH

M	T	W	T	F	S	S
						1
2	3	4	5	6	7	8
9	10	11	12	13	14	15
16	17	18	19	20	21	22
23	24	25	26	27	28	29
30	31					

APRIL

M	T	W	T	F	S	S
		1	2	3	4	5
6	7	8	9	10	11	12
13	14	15	16	17	18	19
20	21	22	23	24	25	26
27	28	29	30			

MAY

M	T	W	T	F	S	S
				1	2	3
4	5	6	7	8	9	10
11	12	13	14	15	16	17
18	19	20	21	22	23	24
25	26	27	28	29	30	31

JUNE

M	T	W	T	F	S	S
1	2	3	4	5	6	7
8	9	10	11	12	13	14
15	16	17	18	19	20	21
22	23	24	25	26	27	28
29	30					

JULY

M	T	W	T	F	S	S
		1	2	3	4	5
6	7	8	9	10	11	12
13	14	15	16	17	18	19
20	21	22	23	24	25	26
27	28	29	30	31		

AUGUST

M	T	W	T	F	S	S
					1	2
3	4	5	6	7	8	9
10	11	12	13	14	15	16
17	18	19	20	21	22	23
24	25	26	27	28	29	30
31						

SEPTEMBER

M	T	W	T	F	S	S
	1	2	3	4	5	6
7	8	9	10	11	12	13
14	15	16	17	18	19	20
21	22	23	24	25	26	27
28	29	30				

OCTOBER

M	T	W	T	F	S	S
			1	2	3	4
5	6	7	8	9	10	11
12	13	14	15	16	17	18
19	20	21	22	23	24	25
26	27	28	29	30	31	

NOVEMBER

M	T	W	T	F	S	S
						1
2	3	4	5	6	7	8
9	10	11	12	13	14	15
16	17	18	19	20	21	22
23	24	25	26	27	28	29
30						

DECEMBER

M	T	W	T	F	S	S
	1	2	3	4	5	6
7	8	9	10	11	12	13
14	15	16	17	18	19	20
21	22	23	24	25	26	27
28	29	30	31			

PERSONAL INFORMATION

NAME:

ADDRESS:

HOME TEL:

MOBILE:

EMAIL:

IN CASE OF EMERGENCY PLEASE CONTACT:

NAME:

ADDRESS:

HOME TEL:

MOBILE:

EMAIL:

DOCTOR:

BLOOD GROUP:

ALLERGIES:

NATIONAL INSURANCE Nº:

CAR REGISTRATION Nº:

PASSPORT Nº:

CONVERSIONS

WEIGHT

METRIC	IMPERIAL
50g	2oz
75g	2½oz
100g	4oz
125g	4½oz
150g	5oz
175g	6oz
200g	7oz
225g	8oz
250g	9oz
300g	11oz
350g	12oz
400g	14oz
450g	1lb
500g	1lb 2oz
550g	1lb 4oz
600g	1lb 5oz
650g	1lb 7oz
700g	1lb 9oz
750g	1lb 10oz
800g	1lb 12oz
850g	1lb 14oz
900g	2lb
950g	2lb 2oz
1kg	2lb 4oz

VOLUME

METRIC	IMPERIAL
30ml	1fl oz
50ml	2fl oz
75ml	2½fl oz
100ml	3½fl oz
125ml	4fl oz
150ml	¼ pint
175ml	6fl oz
200ml	7fl oz
225ml	8fl oz
250ml	9fl oz
300ml	½ pint
350ml	12fl oz
400ml	14fl oz
425ml	¾ pint
450ml	16fl oz
500ml	18fl oz
600ml	1 pint
700ml	1¼ pint
850ml	1½ pint
1 litre	1¾ pint

SPOON MEASURES

METRIC	IMPERIAL
5ml	1tsp
10ml	2tsp
15ml	1tbsp
30ml	2tbsp
45ml	3tbsp
60ml	4tbsp
75ml	5tbsp

TEMPERATURE

GASMARK	°F	°C
¼	250	120
1	275	140
2	300w	150
3	325	160
4	350	180
5	375	190
6	400	200
7	425	220
8	450	230
9	475	240

°F		°C
212	BOILING	100
122		50
113		45
104		40
95		35
86		30
77		25
68		20
59		15
50		10
41		5
32	FREEZING	0

NOTES

SPECIAL DATES

JANUARY

FEBRUARY

MARCH

APRIL

MAY

JUNE

JULY

AUGUST

SEPTEMBER

OCTOBER

NOVEMBER

DECEMBER

SPICED AND ICED CARROT CAKE

A richly flavoured, very moist cake with plenty of spice, sandwiched and topped with a vibrant orange cream cheese icing.

DEC 2014/JAN 2015

29 MONDAY

30 TUESDAY

31 WEDNESDAY

1 THURSDAY

NEW YEAR'S HOLIDAY (UK & REPUBLIC OF IRELAND)

2 FRIDAY

HOLIDAY (SCOTLAND)

3 SATURDAY

4 SUNDAY

SPICED AND ICED CARROT CAKE

INGREDIENTS

FOR THE CAKE

4 large free-range eggs, at room temperature
175ml light olive oil
115g light muscovado sugar
115g dark muscovado sugar
225g plain flour
2½ teaspoons baking powder
½ teaspoon freshly grated nutmeg
1 teaspoon ground cinnamon
¼ teaspoon ground cloves
375g carrots (6-7 medium), coarsely grated
75g walnut pieces
75g desiccated coconut
100g raisins
Finely grated zest of 1 large navel orange

FOR THE CANDIED PEEL

1 large navel orange
20g caster sugar
3 tablespoons water

FOR THE DRIZZLE SYRUP

Juice of 1 large navel orange
Juice of 1 medium lemon
50g caster sugar

FOR THE ICING

135g unsalted butter, at room temperature
200g full-fat cream cheese, at room temperature
115g icing sugar
4 tablespoons Orange Curd, well chilled
50g walnut halves, to decorate

JANUARY

5	MONDAY
6	TUESDAY
7	WEDNESDAY
8	THURSDAY
9	FRIDAY
10	SATURDAY
11	SUNDAY

SPICED AND ICED CARROT CAKE

RECIPE

MAKES 1 LARGE CAKE – YOU WILL NEED: 2 X 20.5CM DEEP SANDWICH TINS, GREASED WITH BUTTER AND BASE-LINED

1 Heat your oven to 180°C/350°F/gas 4. Start by making the cake. Put the eggs, olive oil and both muscovado sugars into a large mixing bowl. Whisk with an electric mixer for 4-5 minutes until very frothy. Sift the flour, baking powder and spices into the bowl and gently fold in with a large metal spoon. Add the carrots, walnut pieces, coconut, raisins and grated zest to the bowl and fold in until thoroughly combined.

2 Spoon the mixture into the prepared tins and spread evenly. Place in the heated oven and bake for 30-35 minutes until a skewer inserted into the centre of each cake comes out clean.

3 While the cake layers are baking, make the candied peel and the drizzle syrup. Using a vegetable peeler, carefully shave strips of coloured peel off the orange, leaving all the white pith on the fruit. Cut the strips into very thin shreds and put them into a small pan. Add water to cover. Bring to the boil, then simmer gently for 10–12 minutes until soft. Drain the shreds, then return them to the pan and add the sugar and 3 tablespoons of water. Heat gently until the sugar has dissolved, then simmer for a few minutes until the mixture becomes thick and syrupy. Pour the candied peel on to a heatproof plate and leave until cold.

4 For the drizzle syrup, put the orange and lemon juices in the rinsed-out pan that you used for the candied peel. Add the sugar and heat gently until it has dissolved, then bring to the boil and boil for 1 minute. Remove from the heat and keep warm.

5 When the cake layers are ready, remove from the oven and set the tins on a wire rack. Prick the cakes all over with a cocktail stick, then quickly spoon 3 tablespoons of the hot drizzle syrup over each cake. Leave to soak in and cool completely in the tins.

6 To make the icing, put the butter into a large bowl and beat thoroughly with an electric mixer or wooden spoon. Beat in the cream cheese until smooth and evenly combined. Sift in the icing sugar and mix in, on low speed if using an electric mixer. Stir in the chilled orange curd. Cover and chill the icing until it is firm enough to spread.

7 When ready to assemble the cake, turn out the cake layers on to a large board. Spread half of the icing over the top of each sponge, then set one on top of the other. Transfer the cake to a serving platter. Swirl the icing on the top of the cake using the handle of a teaspoon. Decorate with the strips of candied peel and walnut halves. Store in an airtight container in a cool spot. Best eaten within 4 days.

ON YOUR *Marks* get set BAKE

JANUARY

12   MONDAY

13   TUESDAY

14   WEDNESDAY

15   THURSDAY

16   FRIDAY

17   SATURDAY

18   SUNDAY

NOTES

JANUARY

19   MONDAY

20   TUESDAY

21   WEDNESDAY

22   THURSDAY

23   FRIDAY

24   SATURDAY

25   SUNDAY

NOTES

JANUARY/FEBRUARY

26   MONDAY

27   TUESDAY

28   WEDNESDAY

29   THURSDAY

30   FRIDAY

31   SATURDAY

1   SUNDAY

UPSIDE-DOWN CAKE

A very light and pretty sponge studded with chunks of fiery
stem ginger and topped with a sticky fruit and nut mix.

FEBRUARY

2   MONDAY

3   TUESDAY

4   WEDNESDAY

5   THURSDAY

6   FRIDAY

7   SATURDAY

8   SUNDAY

PEAR UPSIDE-DOWN CAKE

INGREDIENTS

FOR THE TOPPING

75g pecan nut halves

100g salted butter, thickly sliced

100g dark brown sugar

2-3 lumps stem ginger, finely chopped, plus
1½ tablespoons syrup from the jar

3-4 ripe but firm William's pears

FOR THE CAKE

115g unsalted butter, softened

170g caster sugar

2 large free-range eggs, at
room temperature, beaten

175g plain flour

1½ teaspoons baking powder

¼ teaspoon salt

¼-½ teaspoon ground ginger

125ml milk

1½ teaspoons vanilla extract

2-3 lumps stem ginger, drained and finely
chopped

FOR THE CREAM

225ml double cream, well chilled

25g icing sugar, sifted

1 tablespoon Poire William

1 × 22-23cm deep cake tin (not loose-based)

FEBRUARY

9   MONDAY

10   TUESDAY

11   WEDNESDAY

12   THURSDAY

13   FRIDAY

14   SATURDAY

ST. VALENTINE'S DAY

15   SUNDAY

PEAR UPSIDE-DOWN CAKE

RECIPE

MAKES I LARGE CAKE

I Preheat the oven to 180°C/350°F/gas 4. Toast the pecan nuts in the oven for 3-5minutes until lightly browned. Cool, then chop fairly fine.

2 Spread the butter slices in the cake tin. Scatter the brown sugar on top and add the ginger syrup. Heat in the oven for 5 minutes. Stir the mixture, then return to the oven to heat for another 5 minutes until bubbling.

3 Meanwhile, peel 3 of the pears (you may not need the fourth), leaving them whole. Trim off the base and the stem ends, then cut across each pear to make circular slices about 1.25cm thick. Using an apple corer (or a small round cutter), cut out the cores to make neat circles in the centre of each slice. If necessary, slightly trim each slice of pear to make it circular (or use a round cutter).

4 Arrange large slices of pear over the bottom of the tin, on top of the sugar mixture (we used 11 slices). Then arrange halved (semi-circular) slices to fill in all the gaps. Fill all the centre holes with chopped pecan nuts. Scatter the stem ginger over the top.

5 To make the cake mixture, beat the butter and caster sugar together using a wooden spoon or electric mixer until light and fluffy. Gradually add the eggs, beating well after each addition. Sift the flour, baking powder, salt and ground ginger into another bowl. Add to the egg mixture in 3 batches alternately with the milk, beating on low speed if using a mixer. Add the vanilla and stem ginger and gently mix in.

6 Carefully spoon the cake mixture on top of the pears in the tin – try not to dislodge the nuts. Bake for about 50 minutes until golden brown and a skewer inserted into the centre of the cake comes out clean. Invert the tin onto a plate (take care as the topping can burn if it splashes your skin), then lift it off. Leave the cake to cool.

THE MIX WILL LOOK QUITE WET BEFORE IT GOES INTO THE OVEN – THIS IS HOW IT SHOULD LOOK SO DON'T PANIC!

7 Whip the cream until soft peaks form. Add the icing sugar and Poire William and briefly whip to combine. Spoon into a bowl and serve with the cake.

FEBRUARY

16   MONDAY

17   TUESDAY

18   WEDNESDAY

ASH WEDNESDAY

19   THURSDAY

CHINESE NEW YEAR

20   FRIDAY

21   SATURDAY

22   SUNDAY

NOTES

FEBRUARY/MARCH

23 MONDAY

24 TUESDAY

25 WEDNESDAY

26 THURSDAY

27 FRIDAY

28 SATURDAY

1 SUNDAY

ST. DAVID'S DAY (WALES)

PAUL'S PLAITED LOAF

This is one of Paul's favourite loaves to make. Practise using lengths of string until you get the hang of the plait.

MARCH

2 MONDAY

3 TUESDAY

4 WEDNESDAY

5 THURSDAY

6 FRIDAY

7 SATURDAY

8 SUNDAY

PAUL'S PLAITED LOAF

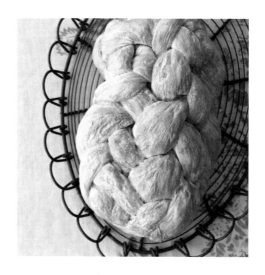

INGREDIENTS

500g strong white bread flour
10g salt
2 x 7g sachets fast-action dried yeast
20ml olive oil
340ml water, at room temperature
1 beaten egg, mixed with a pinch of salt, to glaze
1 baking sheet, dusted with flour

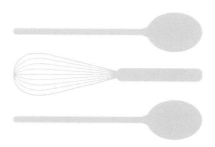

MARCH

9   MONDAY

10   TUESDAY

11   WEDNESDAY

12   THURSDAY

13   FRIDAY

14   SATURDAY

15   SUNDAY

MOTHERING SUNDAY (UK)

PAUL'S PLAITED LOAF

RECIPE
MAKES 1 LOAF

1 Put the flour into a mixing bowl. Put the salt on one side of the bowl and the yeast on the other, making sure they don't touch as the salt can kill the yeast. Add the oil, then stir together with your hand or a spoon until everything is evenly mixed.

2 Add three-quarters of the water and bring the mixture together with your hands. Work in the rest of the water. Knead the dough for about 10 minutes until it is silky and very stretchy. The dough should be slightly soft but not sticky, nor dry and tough.

3 Tip the dough into a lightly oiled bowl, cover tightly with cling film and leave to rise at room temperature for about 1 hour until doubled in size.

4 Punch down (knock back) the risen dough to deflate, then turn it out onto a lightly floured worktop and shape into a ball. Divide into 8 equal pieces. Using your hands, roll each piece on the worktop until it is a thin, sausage-shaped strand about 40cm long.

5 Lay the strands of dough out on the floured worktop like an octopus and tack all the gathered ends to the table with your thumb. As they are laid out in front of you, number them 1-8 and proceed to plait following the sequence below. Note that every time you move a strand, the order of the numbers will revert to the original 1-8 sequence.

STEP 1. Place strand 8 under strand 7, then over strand 1.

STEP 2. Strand 8 over strand 5.

STEP 3. Strand 2 under strand 3, then over strand 8.

STEP 4. Strand 1 over strand 4.

STEP 5. Strand 7 under strand 6 then over strand 1.

Repeat from step 2 until all the strands are plaited, then tuck the ends under the loaf to neaten.

6 Set the plaited loaf on the floured baking sheet and leave to rise at room temperature for about 1 hour until almost doubled in size. Towards the end of the rising time preheat the oven to 200°C/400°F/gas 6.

7 Brush the risen loaf with seasoned beaten egg to glaze, then bake for 20-25 minutes until golden brown and the loaf sounds hollow when tapped on the underside. Cool on a wire rack.

Star Baker

MARCH

16   MONDAY

17   TUESDAY

ST. PATRICK'S DAY HOLIDAY (IRELAND)

18   WEDNESDAY

19   THURSDAY

20   FRIDAY

21   SATURDAY

22   SUNDAY

NOTES

MARCH

23   MONDAY

24   TUESDAY

25   WEDNESDAY

26   THURSDAY

27   FRIDAY

28   SATURDAY

29   SUNDAY

DAYLIGHT SAVING BEGINS

NOTES

MARCH/APRIL

30   MONDAY

31   TUESDAY

1   WEDNESDAY

2   THURSDAY

3   FRIDAY

GOOD FRIDAY (UK)

4   SATURDAY

5   SUNDAY

EASTER SUNDAY

LYCHEE & RASPBERRY TART

There's a lot of work in this elaborate designer tart – rich sweet pastry flavoured with rosewater, praline, an unusual lychee crème pâtissière and tiny macaroons, plus a fluffy mascarpone crème – so allow plenty of time.

APRIL

6   MONDAY

EASTER MONDAY (UK & REPUBLIC OF IRELAND)

7   TUESDAY

8   WEDNESDAY

9   THURSDAY

10   FRIDAY

11   SATURDAY

12   SUNDAY

LYCHEE & RASPBERRY TART

INGREDIENTS

FOR THE SWEET PASTRY
200g plain flour
80g icing sugar
100g salted butter, chilled and diced
2 large free-range egg yolks
About 2 teaspoons rosewater
A little beaten egg, for brushing

FOR THE PRALINE
150g whole blanched almonds
100g caster sugar

FOR THE MACAROONS
75g icing sugar, sifted
75g ground almonds
75g caster sugar
2 large free-range egg whites, at room temperature
Red edible food colouring gel

FOR THE LYCHEE CRÈME PÂTISSIÈRE
500ml full-fat milk
6 large free-range egg yolks, at room temperature

100g caster sugar
3 tablespoons cornflour
25g unsalted butter, at room temperature
1 x 425g tin lychees in light syrup, drained and finely chopped
Icing sugar, to sprinkle

FOR THE CRÈME MASCARPONE
1 large free-range egg, at room temperature
30g caster sugar
2 teaspoons raspberry liqueur
1 teaspoon rosewater
½ teaspoon agar flakes
175g mascarpone, well chilled

TO FINISH
150g fresh raspberries
3 tablespoons seedless (or sieved) raspberry jam, heated
1 x 23cm deep loose-based flan tin; a sugar thermometer; a piping bag plus a 2cm plain tube; a baking sheet lined with baking paper

APRIL

13   MONDAY

14   TUESDAY

15   WEDNESDAY

16   THURSDAY

17   FRIDAY

18   SATURDAY

19   SUNDAY

LYCHEE & RASPBERRY TART

RECIPE

SERVES 10

1 To make the pastry, put the flour and icing sugar into the bowl of a food-processor and 'pulse' a couple of times to combine. Add the diced butter and process until the mixture looks like fine crumbs. With the motor running, add the yolks and rosewater through the feed tube. Stop the machine when the dough comes together in a ball. If there are dry crumbs work in a little more rosewater. Wrap in cling film and chill for 30 minutes.

2 Meanwhile, make the praline (see 'How to Make' page). When cold and set, crush or coarsely chop into pieces the size of your little fingernail. Set aside until needed.

3 Roll out the pastry on a floured worktop and use to line the flan tin. Prick the base and chill for 20 minutes. Meanwhile, preheat the oven to 180°C/350°F/gas 4.

4 Bake the pastry case 'blind'; after removing the paper and beans, lightly brush the inside of the pastry case with beaten egg, then tip about half of the praline into the case and press onto the sides and base. Return the pastry case to the oven and bake for a further 10-12 minutes until the pastry is golden and crisp. Leave to cool but do not turn out. Leave the oven on.

5 To make the macaroons, combine the icing sugar and ground almonds; set aside until needed. Gently heat the caster sugar with 2½ tablespoons water in a small pan until dissolved. Meanwhile, put the egg whites and a little red colouring gel (just dip a cocktail stick into the small pot) into a large mixing bowl and whisk with an electric mixer until soft peaks will form. Bring the sugar syrup to the boil and boil rapidly until it reaches 118°C/245°F on a sugar thermometer, then slowly pour onto the egg whites in a thin, steady stream while whisking on full speed, to make a thick, glossy meringue. Continue whisking until the meringue cools to room temperature, then fold in the icing sugar mixture.

6 Spoon the meringue mixture into the piping bag fitted with the 2cm plain tube and pipe tiny macaroons – about 2.5cm across – on the lined baking sheet (you'll be able to pipe about 48 macaroons). Leave to stand for 15 minutes to form a crust, then bake for about 12 minutes until firm but not turning brown. Leave to cool on the sheet.

Recipe continues overleaf

APRIL

20 MONDAY

21 TUESDAY

22 WEDNESDAY

23 THURSDAY

ST. GEORGE'S DAY (ENGLAND)

24 FRIDAY

25 SATURDAY

26 SUNDAY

LYCHEE & RASPBERRY TART
RECIPE

7 Next make the crème pâtissière (see 'How to Make' page). Once the custard has thickened, remove from the heat and leave to cool for 10 minutes before stirring in the butter and lychees. Transfer the mixture to a bowl. Sprinkle the surface with icing sugar to prevent a skin from forming, then cover and chill for at least 1 hour.

8 Meanwhile, make the crème mascarpone. Put the egg and sugar into a medium-sized heatproof bowl set over a pan of boiling water and whisk with a hand-held electric mixer until frothy and just slightly too hot for your finger to bear comfortably. Add the liqueur, rosewater and agar flakes, then continue whisking until the mixture is thick enough to a leave a ribbon-like trail when the whisk is lifted; take care not to let the mixture get too hot and start to scramble. Remove the bowl, set it in iced water and whisk until cold. Whisk in the mascarpone, then cover and chill until ready to assemble.

9 Lightly brush or paint each raspberry with hot raspberry jam and leave to set on a sheet of baking paper.

10 To assemble the tart, unmould the pastry case and set it on a serving platter. Stir the crème pâtissière until creamy, then spoon into the pastry case and spread out evenly.

11 Carefully spread the crème mascarpone over the top of the crème pâtissière. Arrange the glazed raspberries on top in straight parallel lines, leaving a raspberry's width between each line. Finish with macaroons – you won't need them all – and the rest of the praline. Serve as soon as possible; best eaten the same day.

APRIL/MAY

---

27 MONDAY

---

28 TUESDAY

---

29 WEDNESDAY

---

30 THURSDAY

---

1 FRIDAY

---

2 SATURDAY

---

3 SUNDAY

PEACH FRANGIPANE TART

This classic combination of fruit and frangipane is baked in a pastry case made from pâte sucrée – a richer and sweeter version of the pâte brisée. There's no water, just egg yolks, and extra sugar, which give the pastry a sandy, biscuit-like taste and texture. Because of the extra sugar the pastry colours more quickly so it is baked at a lower temperature.

MAY

4   MONDAY

MAY DAY HOLIDAY (UK & REPUBLIC OF IRELAND)

5   TUESDAY

6   WEDNESDAY

7   THURSDAY

8   FRIDAY

9   SATURDAY

10   SUNDAY

PEACH FRANGIPANE TART

INGREDIENTS

FOR THE PÂTE SUCRÉE

200g plain flour

¼ teaspoon salt

100g unsalted butter, chilled

4 large free-range egg yolks

100g caster sugar

Finely grated zest of ½ unwaxed lemon

FOR THE FILLING

100g unsalted butter, softened

100g caster sugar

Finely grated zest of ½ unwaxed lemon

2 large free-range eggs, beaten

100g ground almonds

100g plain flour

4 medium just-ripe peaches

1 tablespoon flaked almonds, to decorate
icing sugar, for dusting

1 x 23cm deep loose-based flan tin; a baking
sheet

MAY

11   MONDAY

12   TUESDAY

13   WEDNESDAY

14   THURSDAY

15   FRIDAY

16   SATURDAY

17   SUNDAY

PEACH FRANGIPANE TART

RECIPE

SERVES 8

1 Make up the Pâte Sucrée (see 'How to make' page), but omitting the water and adding the lemon zest to the well with the other ingredients. The dough will feel slightly stickier than pâte brisée, but avoid flouring your hands as much as possible. After the dough has been worked and is silky-smooth and pliable, wrap and chill for 30 minutes until firm.

2 Lightly dust the worktop with flour, then roll out the pastry to a circle and use to line the flan tin. Save any pastry trimmings to use for decoration. Prick the base of the pastry case, then chill while preparing the filling. Preheat the oven to 190°C/375°F/gas 5 and put the baking sheet into the oven to heat up.

3 Put the butter into a mixing bowl and beat with a wooden spoon or electric mixer until creamy. Add the sugar and lemon zest and beat until the mixture becomes very light in colour and texture. Gradually add the eggs, beating well after each addition. Fold in the ground almonds and flour with a large metal spoon. When thoroughly combined, spoon the mixture into the pastry case and spread evenly. Keep in the fridge while preparing the peaches.

4 Bring a pan of water to the boil. Make a small nick in the skin of each peach at the stalk end, then gently place it in the boiling water. Leave for 12 seconds, then remove. Once the peaches are cool enough to handle, slip off their skins. Halve the fruit and remove the stones.

5 Set 7 of the peach halves, rounded side up, on top of the almond filling. Cut the remaining half into thick slices, leaving them attached at the stalk end, and arrange in a fan shape in the centre of the tart. Set the tin on the hot baking sheet and bake for 25 minutes.

6 While the tart is baking, re-roll the pastry trimmings and cut into leaf shapes with a cutter (or cut round a template or free-hand). Remove the tart from the oven – the almond filling will have puffed up around the fruit – and lay the pastry decorations on top. Scatter over the flaked almonds. Dust with icing sugar and return to the oven. Reduce the temperature to 180°C/350°F/gas 4 and bake for a further 25–30 minutes until the pastry and almond filling are golden.

7 Remove from the oven and leave to cool for 10 minutes before carefully unmoulding; the frangipane filling will gradually subside. Serve the tart warm the same day or the next, either at room temperature or reheated in a 160°C/325°F/gas 3 oven for 10–12 minutes.

MAY

18 MONDAY

19 TUESDAY

20 WEDNESDAY

21 THURSDAY

22 FRIDAY

23 SATURDAY

24 SUNDAY

NOTES

MAY

25 MONDAY

SPRING HOLIDAY (UK)

26 TUESDAY

27 WEDNESDAY

28 THURSDAY

29 FRIDAY

30 SATURDAY

31 SUNDAY

NOTES

JUNE

1   MONDAY

2   TUESDAY

3   WEDNESDAY

4   THURSDAY

5   FRIDAY

6   SATURDAY

7   SUNDAY

HAZELNUT TORTE

A rich but not heavy concoction with an intriguing flavour
– plenty of chocolate and nuts with a dash of passion fruit.

JUNE

8 MONDAY

9 TUESDAY

10 WEDNESDAY

11 THURSDAY

12 FRIDAY

13 SATURDAY

14 SUNDAY

HAZELNUT TORTE

INGREDIENTS

FOR THE SPONGE

250g unsalted butter, at room temperature, diced

255g dark chocolate (about 70% cocoa solids), chopped

3 passion fruit

160g hazelnuts

6 large free-range eggs, at room temperature, separated

200g caster sugar

FOR THE GANACHE

300ml double cream

4 passion fruit

300g dark chocolate (about 70% cocoa solids),
chopped cocoa powder, for dusting

1 × 23cm springclip tin, greased and the base lined with baking paper

JUNE

15   **MONDAY**

16   **TUESDAY**

17   **WEDNESDAY**

18   **THURSDAY**

19   **FRIDAY**

20   **SATURDAY**

21   **SUNDAY**

FATHER'S DAY / LONGEST DAY

HAZELNUT TORTE

RECIPE
SERVES 12-16

1 Preheat the oven to 160°C/325°F/gas 3. Put the butter and chocolate into a heatproof bowl. Halve the passion fruit and scoop the pulp and seeds into a sieve set over the bowl. Press to extract the juice; discard the seeds. Set the bowl over a pan of steaming hot but not boiling water and melt gently. Remove the bowl from the pan and cool.

2 Grind 120g of the hazelnuts in a food-processor to a fine powder. Add the remaining 40g nuts and 'pulse' 3 or 4 times to roughly chop. Set aside until needed.

3 Whisk the egg whites with an electric mixer until they stand in soft peaks. Whisk in a tablespoon of the weighed sugar until stiff and glossy. Whisk the yolks with the remaining sugar until the mixture is very pale and thick, and will make a ribbon trail.

4 Using a large metal spoon, fold the chocolate mixture into the yolk mixture. When thoroughly combined fold in the nuts. Finally, fold in the egg whites in 3 batches.

5 Spoon the mixture into the prepared tin and spread evenly. Bake for 45–55 minutes until a skewer inserted in the centre comes out clean. Cool in the tin for 5 minutes – the torte will shrink slightly – then turn out onto a wire rack and leave to cool completely.

6 To make the ganache, put the cream into a pan. Halve the passion fruit and scoop out the pulp and seeds into the cream. Heat until the cream just comes to the boil, then remove from the heat and leave to infuse while melting the chocolate.

7 The cream and chocolate should be the same temperature, so gently warm the cream if it has cooled too much. Strain the cream into the chocolate to remove the passion fruit seeds and stir until the ganache is smooth and glossy. It should thicken slightly but still be pourable.

8 Set the torte upside down on a serving platter (the flat underside makes a better surface for covering). Pour four-fifths of the ganache onto the cake and let it flow evenly over the top and down the sides, helping it as little as possible. Leave to set, then clean up the excess ganache.

9 Leave the remaining ganache to thicken until almost setting, then drop teaspoons onto a sheet of baking paper. Once firm, dust your hands with cocoa powder and roll into neat small balls. Arrange around the edge of the cake and dust the whole torte with cocoa powder. Can be kept, well covered, in a cool spot – not the fridge – for up to 48 hours.

JUNE

22 MONDAY

23 TUESDAY

24 WEDNESDAY

25 THURSDAY

26 FRIDAY

27 SATURDAY

28 SUNDAY

NOTES

JUNE/JULY

29 MONDAY

30 TUESDAY

1 WEDNESDAY

2 THURSDAY

3 FRIDAY

4 SATURDAY

5 SUNDAY

ZEBRA CAKE

A great cake for a party –
just add candles! The sponge
is a quick all-in-one mix
with half flavoured with
cocoa, the other with vanilla.
The mixtures are piped in
stripes into sandwich tins.

JULY

6 MONDAY

7 TUESDAY

8 WEDNESDAY

9 THURSDAY

10 FRIDAY

11 SATURDAY

12 SUNDAY

ZEBRA CAKE

INGREDIENTS

225g unsalted butter, at room temperature

225g caster sugar

4 eggs, at room temperature

225g self-raising flour

½ teaspoon vanilla extract

2½ tablespoons milk

3 tablespoons cocoa powder

FOR THE FILLING

100g unsalted butter, at room temperature

275g icing sugar

½ teaspoon vanilla extract

3 teaspoons milk

2 tablespoons cocoa powder

YOU WILL ALSO NEED

Large bowl for mixing

Wooden spoon or hand-held electric mixer

Plastic or rubber scraper

Medium bowl

4 disposable piping bags

2 mugs or jugs

Kitchen scissors

2 × 20.5cm sandwich tins, greased with butter and the base lined with baking paper

Wire rack

Large sieve

JULY

13 MONDAY

HOLIDAY (NORTHERN IRELAND)

14 TUESDAY

15 WEDNESDAY

16 THURSDAY

17 FRIDAY

18 SATURDAY

19 SUNDAY

ZEBRA CAKE
RECIPE
MAKES 1 LARGE CAKE

1 Preheat the oven to 180°C/350°F/gas 4. Put the soft butter and caster sugar into the mixing bowl. Add the eggs and flour. Beat everything together with the wooden spoon or electric mixer until smooth and even in colour. Stop and scrape down the sides of the bowl from time to time so everything is thoroughly combined.

2 Divide the mixture in half. Scrape one portion into the medium bowl and stir in the vanilla and 1 tablespoon of the milk.

3 Fold down the top quarter of one of the piping bags. Scrape the vanilla cake mixture into the bag. Unfold the top quarter and twist the bag at the top to prevent the mixture from escaping. Leave the bag standing in a mug while you make up the choc mixture.

4 Add the cocoa and the remaining 1 ½ tablespoons milk to the rest of the cake mixture and beat in well. Fill another piping bag with this mixture.

5 Now you are ready to start piping! Snip the tip off each bag to make an opening 2.5cm across.

6 Twist the top of the bag of white vanilla mix to force the mixture down to the end. With one hand, hold the bag upright over one of the prepared tins; use the other hand to squeeze the bag and pipe a stripe of mixture straight down the centre of the tin. Do the same

thing in the other tin.

7 Next pipe a line of chocolate on each side of the white stripe, so the mixtures just touch. Then pipe a white stripe next to each choc stripe. Keep doing this until the tin is filled, then go back and fill in any gaps. With luck, you should get 4 stripes of each colour in each tin.

8 Place in the heated oven and bake for 20–25 minutes until the vanilla sponge stripes are golden. To test if the sponges are cooked, use the fingertip test; if necessary, bake for a few more minutes, then test again.

9 Set the tins on a heatproof surface and cool for 5 minutes, then turn out of the tins onto the wire rack. Peel off the lining paper and leave to cool completely.

10 Meanwhile, make the filling. Put the soft butter into the washed mixing bowl. Sift the icing sugar into the bowl. Beat together using the washed wooden spoon, or electric mixer on low speed (to avoid a cloud of icing sugar), until very smooth and paler in colour.

11 Scrape half the filling into the washed medium bowl. Add the vanilla and 1 teaspoon of the milk and beat until smooth and creamy. Fill a piping bag in the same way as before.

Recipe continues overleaf

JULY

20 MONDAY

21 TUESDAY

22 WEDNESDAY

23 THURSDAY

24 FRIDAY

25 SATURDAY

26 SUNDAY

ZEBRA CAKE
RECIPE

12 Sift the cocoa into the rest of the filling, then add the remaining 2 teaspoons of milk and mix well until evenly coloured and creamy. Fill the last piping bag.

13 Take a look at the 2 sponges (which are upside down on the wire rack). You want dramatic black and white stripes on top of the cake, so pick the sponge with the best-looking stripes for the top layer. Set the other sponge on a board or serving platter.

14 Snip the ends off the piping bags to make an opening 2cm across, then pipe stripes of icing over the bottom cake – in the same way as you did before. Set the other sponge gently on top. Store in an airtight container and eat within 5 days.

BAKING IN PROGRESS

JULY/AUGUST

27 MONDAY

28 TUESDAY

29 WEDNESDAY

30 THURSDAY

31 FRIDAY

1 SATURDAY

2 SUNDAY

SIXPENCE CAKE

This witty cake, based on the nursery rhyme about blackbirds baked in a pie, is made from 4 sponge cakes sandwiched with butter icing. When you cut you'll see the blackbird with the maid's nose in its beak. The 'pie' top and dish are actually painted sugar paste icing.

AUGUST

3   MONDAY

HOLIDAY (SCOTLAND & REPUBLIC OF IRELAND)

4   TUESDAY

5   WEDNESDAY

6   THURSDAY

7   FRIDAY

8   SATURDAY

9   SUNDAY

SIXPENCE CAKE

INGREDIENTS

FOR THE MAIN SPONGE CAKE
350g unsalted butter, softened
350g caster sugar
Finely grated zest of 1½ lemons
6 large free-range eggs, at room temperature, beaten
350g self-raising flour

FOR THE COLOURED SPONGES
115g unsalted butter, softened
115g caster sugar
Finely grated zest of ½ lemon
2 large free-range eggs, at room temperature, beaten
115g self-raising flour
Black, yellow and flesh-pink edible food colouring gels

FOR THE BUTTER ICING
250g unsalted butter, softened
350g icing sugar, sifted
Finely grated zest and juice of 1 lemon

TO FINISH
1kg white ready-to-roll sugar paste icing
Brown edible food colouring gel
Gold lustre
2–4 x 20.5cm sandwich tins, greased and the base lined with baking paper (see recipe)
A small ovenproof bowl (base about 7cm, top about 10cm), greased
A muffin tray
2 paper muffin cases
5cm and 3cm round biscuit cutters

AUGUST

10 MONDAY

11 TUESDAY

12 WEDNESDAY

13 THURSDAY

14 FRIDAY

15 SATURDAY

16 SUNDAY

SIXPENCE CAKE

RECIPE

MAKES I CAKE

I Preheat the oven to 180°C/350°F/ gas 4. Make the main sponge layers first. Using an electric mixer, beat the butter with the sugar and lemon zest until light. Gradually add the eggs, beating well after each addition. Fold in the flour with a large spoon. Divide into 4 and use one portion for each sponge layer: spoon into the tins and spread evenly, then bake for 25 minutes until firm when gently pressed in the centre. Cool on a wire rack. (If you don't have 4 tins, bake in batches; use a cold, clean prepared tin for each sponge.)

2 Make the mixture for the coloured sponges in the same way. Transfer half to another mixing bowl and colour it black. Spoon into the prepared ovenproof bowl and bake for about 30 minutes until firm when gently pressed. Leave for 5 minutes, then carefully unmould onto a wire rack and cool.

3 Divide the rest of the cake mixture in half. Colour one portion yellow (for the bird's beak) and the other portion flesh-pink (for the maid's nose). Spoon each into a muffin case (set in the muffin tray). Bake for about 25 minutes until firm. Leave to cool, in the muffin cases, on a wire rack.

4 Make the butter icing by beating all the ingredients together until smooth, very soft and spreadable. Set aside, but do not chill.

5 To assemble the 'pie', set one sponge layer upside down on the worktop and spread butter icing over the top surface. Use the 5cm cutter to cut a round hole from the centre of 2 of the other sponge layers, then sandwich them together with butter icing. Set on top of the first sponge layer.

6 Peel off the paper cases from the 2 small coloured sponges and turn them upside down on the worktop. With the 5cm cutter, cut a cylinder 5cm deep from the centre of the yellow sponge. Use the 3cm cutter to remove the centre of this cylinder – do not cut all the way through; the sponge should look like a bucket. With the 3cm cutter, cut a cylinder 5cm deep from the small pink sponge and gently press it into the hole in the yellow cylinder; trim level. Spread butter icing over the outside of this new cylinder, then press it upside down (yellow side up) into the hole in the 2 sponge layers so all you can see is a yellow disc in the middle. Spread with butter icing.

Recipe continues overleaf

AUGUST

17   MONDAY

18   TUESDAY

19   WEDNESDAY

20   THURSDAY

21   FRIDAY

22   SATURDAY

23   SUNDAY

SIXPENCE CAKE
RECIPE

7 Trim the top of the black sponge to make it 3cm high and 10cm across the top (flat) surface. This will be the blackbird. Stand the ovenproof bowl in the centre of the fourth sponge layer and cut around it to remove a disc the size of the black sponge. Spread the curved, rounded surfaces of the black sponge with butter icing and press into the hole. Set on top of the other 3 sponge layers.

8 Trim the lower 2 layers of sponge so the sides slope in to resemble a pie dish. Trim the edges of the top sponge layer so the middle looks rounded like a well-filled pie. Spread butter icing over the whole cake.

9 Dust a spotlessly clean worktop with icing sugar, then roll out 250g of the sugar paste icing to a strip about 7 x 64cm. Measure the height of the 'pie dish' section of the cake, and the circumference, then cut the strip to fit exactly. Gently press the strip around the lower part of the cake, moulding and smoothing it so it looks like a china pie dish.

10 Colour 120g of the sugar paste icing a creamy brown, then roll with your hands to a sausage about 1cm thick and 64cm long. Press this around the top edge of the cake – this is the 'pastry rim' – so it covers the top edge of the white icing strip.

11 Colour 500g of the remaining sugar paste icing a beige-brown colour – this will be the 'pastry lid' – then roll out to a large circle the thickness of a pound coin. Cut out a neat circle 25cm across and set on top of the cake. Press onto the rim to seal, then crimp or flute. Cut a cross in the centre of the 'pie crust' and lift back the 4 flaps.

12 Colour about 15g sugar paste icing black, then roll into 3 balls – these are the blackbirds' heads. Colour another 15g icing yellow and shape into 3 cones; attach one to each ball (use a dab of water if necessary). Snip the cones with scissors to make the beaks. Set in the exposed centre of the cake.

13 To finish the decoration, paint the edges of the pie with brown colouring to give a 'baked pie' effect, and add dots of colour as pattern for the 'pie dish'. Colour a little more icing black, roll out thinly and cut 5 leaf shapes; slice the edges using a sharp knife or scalpel to resemble feathers, then add to the pie. Use the rest of the icing to make the king's moneybag, coins, the maid's clothes' peg and the queen's slice of bread and honey, colouring and painting them, if you like, to serve with the cake.

AUGUST

24   MONDAY

25   TUESDAY

26   WEDNESDAY

27   THURSDAY

28   FRIDAY

29   SATURDAY

30   SUNDAY

NOTES

AUGUST/SEPTEMBER

31 MONDAY

LATE SUMMER HOLIDAY (UK)

1 TUESDAY

2 WEDNESDAY

3 THURSDAY

4 FRIDAY

5 SATURDAY

6 SUNDAY

SWAN LAKE

These elegant pastry swans, dusted with icing sugar and floating on a lake of raspberry sauce, are as pretty as a picture. Each swan is shaped from 2 pieces of choux pastry: an oval-shaped mound for the body and wings, and a piped S-shape for the head and neck. With their filling of vanilla-flavoured whipped cream and sweet strawberries, the swans are quite special.

SEPTEMBER

7   MONDAY

8   TUESDAY

9   WEDNESDAY

10   THURSDAY

11   FRIDAY

12   SATURDAY

13   SUNDAY

SWAN LAKE

INGREDIENTS

1 quantity Choux Dough

Beaten egg, to glaze

10 large ripe strawberries, at room temperature, thinly sliced
1 quantity Chantilly Cream

FOR THE RASPBERRY SAUCE

250g fresh raspberries

1 teaspoon lemon juice

4 tablespoons icing sugar, or to taste

1 piping bag plus a 6–7mm plain tube and a large star tube (optional);
2 baking sheets, lined with baking paper

SEPTEMBER

14   MONDAY

ROSH HASHANAH (JEWISH NEW YEAR)

15   TUESDAY

16   WEDNESDAY

17   THURSDAY

18   FRIDAY

19   SATURDAY

20   SUNDAY

SWAN LAKE

RECIPE

MAKES 10

1 Make the Choux Dough (see 'How to Make' page). Preheat the oven to 200°C/400°F/gas 6. Spoon some of the dough into the piping bag fitted with the small plain tube (you could also use a disposable piping bag with the tip snipped off). To form the necks for the swans, pipe 12 S shapes (extra to allow for breakages), each about 9cm long, on one of the prepared baking sheets, setting them well apart to allow for expansion. Brush very lightly with beaten egg to glaze, taking care not to 'glue' the dough to the paper. Bake for about 15 minutes until a good golden brown and very crisp. Leave to cool on a wire rack.

2 Return any leftover dough from piping the necks to the rest of the choux dough. To make the bodies, spoon the dough (using 2 kitchen spoons) onto the other baking sheet to make 10 ovals about 8cm long, 4cm wide and 2.5cm high. Set the shapes well apart to allow for expansion. Brush lightly with egg glaze as before and bake for about 30 minutes until a good golden brown.

3 Reduce the oven temperature to 180°C/350°F/gas 4. Open and quickly close the oven door to let out the steam, then bake for a further 5 minutes until the cracks are also coloured. Remove the baking sheets from the oven and make a small hole at one end of each oval to let the steam escape. Return to the oven and bake for another 5 minutes or so until really crisp and dry. Cool on a wire rack. (The cooled baked choux shapes can be kept in a dry airy spot, lightly covered, for up to 4 hours before assembling the swans.)

4 To make the sauce, put the raspberries, lemon juice and icing sugar into a food-processor and purée. Press through a fine sieve to remove the seeds. Taste and add more sugar if needed. Cover and chill for up to 12 hours.

5 When ready to assemble, spoon a little pool of raspberry sauce onto each individual serving plate. Cut the choux ovals in half horizontally, then slice the top section in half lengthways to make the wings. Arrange the sliced strawberries in the base of each oval. Spoon the Chantilly cream into the piping bag fitted with the star tube and pipe cream over the berries to cover (or simply spoon the cream neatly on top of the strawberries). Gently stick a neck into one end of each oval, then set pairs of wings into the cream, on either side of the neck, at an angle so they tilt upwards. Dust with icing sugar and set a swan on the sauce on each plate. Serve as soon as possible.

SEPTEMBER

21 MONDAY

THE UNITED NATIONS INTERNATIONAL DAY OF PEACE

22 TUESDAY

23 WEDNESDAY

YOM KIPPUR (DAY OF ATONEMENT)

24 THURSDAY

25 FRIDAY

26 SATURDAY

27 SUNDAY

NOTES

SEPTEMBER/OCTOBER

28 MONDAY

29 TUESDAY

30 WEDNESDAY

1 THURSDAY

2 FRIDAY

3 SATURDAY

4 SUNDAY

LARDY CAKES

With their crisp, sweet exteriors, light and flaky crumb and spicy, fruit-filled centres, these are high-class lardy cakes.

OCTOBER

5   MONDAY

6   TUESDAY

7   WEDNESDAY

8   THURSDAY

9   FRIDAY

10   SATURDAY

11   SUNDAY

LARDY CAKES

INGREDIENTS

FOR THE DOUGH

170ml milk, plus extra for brushing

40g unsalted butter, cubed

About 375g strong white bread flour

1 teaspoon salt

2 tablespoons caster sugar

9g fast-action dried yeast
(from 2 × 7g sachets)

1 small egg, at room temperature

FOR THE FILLING

250g lard, at room temperature

200g caster sugar

¾ teaspoon ground cinnamon

150g dried mixed fruit, soaked in
2 tablespoons water

TO FINISH

Caster sugar and ground cinnamon

1-3 non-stick 4-hole Yorkshire Pudding tins
(see recipe), buttered and dusted with sugar

OCTOBER

12   MONDAY

13   TUESDAY

14   WEDNESDAY

AL HIJRA

15   THURSDAY

16   FRIDAY

17   SATURDAY

18   SUNDAY

LARDY CAKES

1 Gently warm the milk with the butter until the butter melts, then set aside to cool to lukewarm. Mix the flour with the salt, sugar and yeast in a large mixing bowl or the bowl of a large free-standing electric mixer. Whisk the egg into the buttery milk until combined, then add to the bowl. Work the mixture with your hand, or the dough hook attachment, to make a very soft but not sticky dough. If necessary, gradually work in extra flour a tablespoon at a time.

2 Turn out the dough onto a lightly floured worktop and knead thoroughly by hand for 10 minutes, or 5 minutes with the dough hook on low speed. Return the dough to the clean bowl, cover with clingfilm and leave to rise in a warm place for about 1 hour until doubled in size.

3 Meanwhile, mash the soft lard with the sugar and cinnamon on a large plate to make a soft, very spreadable paste. Divide it into 20 (this makes it easier to use later).

4 Punch down the risen dough to deflate, then divide into 10 equal portions. Shape each into a neat ball. Roll out one of the balls on a lightly floured worktop to a circle about 14cm across. Spread with one portion of the lard mixture (as if you were buttering bread). Fold about one-sixth of the edge of the circle into the centre. Repeat the folding all the way around, rotating the circle, so it becomes a hexagon. Roll out to a 14cm circle again. Repeat with the other 9 balls of dough. Cover the circles with a sheet of clingfilm and leave to rest for 10 minutes.

5 Uncover the circles and spread each with another portion of the lard mixture, then top with the dried fruit mixture (drain off any excess liquid first). Fold the edges of each circle to make hexagons as before.

6 Place each hexagon, with the side with the folded edges uppermost, into a hole in the prepared tin(s). Cover lightly with clingfilm and leave in a warm place to rise for about 45 minutes until doubled in size. (If you have only one 4-hole tin you can bake in batches; spread the rest of the prepared lardy cakes on a baking sheet lined with baking paper and keep them, lightly covered, in a cool spot so they rise slowly, then bake them in batches in the prepared tin.) Towards the end of the rising time preheat the oven to 200°C/400°F/gas 6.

7 Brush the lardy cakes lightly with milk and bake for 15 minutes until golden brown. Turn off the oven, and quickly open and close the oven door (to let out a bit of heat and steam). Leave the cakes in the oven for 5 minutes. Cool in the tin for 10 minutes, then turn out onto a wire rack. Sprinkle with sugar and cinnamon and leave until just warm before eating. Best the same day.

OCTOBER

19   MONDAY

20   TUESDAY

21   WEDNESDAY

22   THURSDAY

23   FRIDAY

24   SATURDAY

25   SUNDAY

DAYLIGHT SAVING ENDS

NOTES

OCTOBER/NOVEMBER

26   MONDAY

HOLIDAY (REPUBLIC OF IRELAND)

27   TUESDAY

28   WEDNESDAY

29   THURSDAY

30   FRIDAY

31   SATURDAY

HALLOWEEN

1   SUNDAY

CHELSEA BUNS

Not your usual Chelsea bun! These baked beauties are brimful of dried fruits and finished with an apricot glaze and orange icing.

NOVEMBER

2   MONDAY

3   TUESDAY

4   WEDNESDAY

5   THURSDAY

6   FRIDAY

7   SATURDAY

8   SUNDAY

REMEMBRANCE SUNDAY

CHELSEA BUNS

INGREDIENTS

FOR THE DOUGH

500g strong white bread flour, plus extra for dusting

1 teaspoon salt

1 x 7g sachet fast-action dried yeast

300ml milk

40g unsalted butter, softened

1 free-range egg, at room temperature

Vegetable oil

FOR THE FILLING

25g unsalted butter, melted

Grated zest of 1 orange

75g soft brown sugar

2 teaspoons ground cinnamon

100g dried cranberries

100g sultanas

100g dried apricots, chopped

TO FINISH

1 heaped tablespoon apricot jam

200g icing sugar, sifted

Grated zest of 1 orange

1 deep baking tray, lightly greased

NOVEMBER

9   MONDAY

10   TUESDAY

11   WEDNESDAY

DIWALI

12   THURSDAY

13   FRIDAY

14   SATURDAY

15   SUNDAY

CHELSEA BUNS

RECIPE

MAKES 10

1 Put the flour and salt into a large mixing bowl. Make a well in the middle and add the yeast. Heat the milk and butter in a saucepan until the butter melts and the mixture is lukewarm. Add to the flour mixture with the egg and stir until the contents of the bowl come together as a soft dough. (If the dough is too wet, you may need to add a little extra flour.)

2 Tip the dough onto a generously floured worktop. Knead for 5 minutes, adding more flour if necessary, until the dough is smooth and elastic and no longer feels sticky.

3 Wash the mixing bowl and lightly grease with a little vegetable oil. Place the dough in the bowl and turn until it is covered all over with oil. Cover the bowl with clingfilm and leave the dough to rise in a warm place for 1 hour until doubled in size.

4 Punch down the dough to its original size, then turn out onto a lightly floured worktop. Roll out the dough to a rectangle about 40cm long and 5mm thick; it should lie horizontally in front of you. Brush all over with the melted butter. Evenly sprinkle the orange zest over the buttered surface, followed by the sugar, cinnamon and fruits.

5 Tack down the long side of the dough rectangle nearest to you (this means pressing it down with your thumb so that it sticks to the table. This will

help you roll the dough). Begin to roll the opposite long side towards you, tightening the roll each time you turn it – use the tacked-down edge to help you tighten the roll. Cut across into 10 pieces about 4cm wide. Place them cut side up in the baking tray, leaving a little space around each slice. Cover with a tea towel and set aside in a warm place to rise for 30 minutes.

6 Preheat the oven to 190°C/375°F/gas 5. Bake the buns for 20–25 minutes until risen and golden brown. Check after 15 minutes and cover the buns with foil if they are getting too brown. Transfer the buns to a wire rack and leave to cool.

7 Put the jam in a small saucepan with a splash of water and melt gently until smooth. Brush the jam over the buns to glaze. Allow to cool.

8 Mix together the icing sugar, orange zest and 2 tablespoons water. Drizzle the icing over the cooled buns and allow to set before serving. Best eaten the same day.

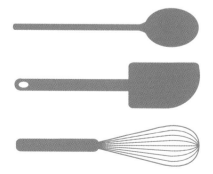

NOVEMBER

16   MONDAY

17   TUESDAY

18   WEDNESDAY

19   THURSDAY

20   FRIDAY

21   SATURDAY

22   SUNDAY

NOTES

NOVEMBER

23 MONDAY

24 TUESDAY

25 WEDNESDAY

26 THURSDAY

27 FRIDAY

28 SATURDAY

29 SUNDAY

NOTES

NOVEMBER/DECEMBER

30   MONDAY

ST. ANDREW'S DAY (SCOTLAND)

1   TUESDAY

2   WEDNESDAY

3   THURSDAY

4   FRIDAY

5   SATURDAY

6   SUNDAY

TRIPLE CHOCOLATE LOG

This rich and spectacular dessert will win you many friends this holiday season. A light sponge rolled around dark and white chocolate mousse layers, it's topped with stunning chocolate and gold leaves. Set aside an afternoon of leisurely baking to rustle this up and prink away with those chocolate leaves to your heart's delight.

DECEMBER

7   MONDAY

8   TUESDAY

9   WEDNESDAY

10   THURSDAY

11   FRIDAY

12   SATURDAY

13   SUNDAY

TRIPLE CHOCOLATE LOG

INGREDIENTS

FOR THE SPONGE

6 large free-range eggs, at room temperature

Good pinch of cream of tartar

140g caster sugar

50g cocoa powder

1–2 tablespoons dark rum (optional)

FOR THE DARK MOUSSE

200g dark chocolate (about 70% cocoa solids), chopped

4 large eggs, at room temperature, separated

1–2 tablespoons dark rum (optional)

1 tablespoon caster sugar

FOR THE WHITE MOUSSE

200ml whipping cream, well chilled

½ teaspoon vanilla extract

75g best-quality white chocolate, well chilled, finely grated

TO FINISH

75g dark chocolate (about 70% cocoa solids), broken up

Edible gold lustre

Cocoa powder, for sprinkling

1 swiss roll tin, baking tray or roasting tin, 25 × 30.5cm (see recipe); parchment-lined foil or baking paper

DECEMBER

14   MONDAY

15   TUESDAY

16   WEDNESDAY

17   THURSDAY

18   FRIDAY

19   SATURDAY

20   SUNDAY

TRIPLE CHOCOLATE LOG

RECIPE

MAKES 10–12

1 Preheat the oven to 190°C/375°F/ gas 5. Line the tin or tray with the parchment-lined foil or baking paper, folding it so it makes a 25 x 30.5cm rectangular container with 2cm sides (it doesn't matter if your tin or tray is larger than this; just make sure the 'liner' is the right size).

2 Make the sponge first. Separate the eggs, putting the whites into a large mixing bowl or the bowl of a large free-standing electric mixer, and the yolks in another. Using an electric mixer, whisk the egg whites until frothy. Add the cream of tartar and continue whisking until the whites stand in stiff peaks. Whisk in 3 tablespoons of the measured caster sugar, a tablespoon at a time, to make a stiff, glossy meringue. Set aside until needed.

3 Add the remaining caster sugar to the egg yolks and whisk with the same beaters (no need to wash) until the mixture is very thick and mousse-like and forms a thick ribbonlike trail when the beaters are lifted from the bowl. Sift the cocoa powder into the bowl and gently fold in with a large metal spoon. Fold the whisked egg whites into the yolk mixture in 3 batches.

4 Transfer the mixture to the prepared 'liner' and spread evenly. Bake for 15–18 minutes until the sponge is springy when gently pressed. Meanwhile, cover a wire rack with a clean, dry tea towel topped with a sheet of baking paper.

5 Tip the baked sponge out onto the lined rack and peel off the paper 'liner'. Sprinkle the rum over the sponge, if using, then leave to cool completely.

6 Meanwhile, make the dark mousse. Melt the chocolate with 100ml water in a large bowl. Off the heat, gently stir in the egg yolks, one at a time, followed by the rum, if using. Whisk the egg whites until stiff as before, then whisk in the sugar. Very gently fold the whites into the chocolate mixture in 3 batches. Cover and chill for 30 minutes until starting to set.

SHOW STOPPER

Recipe continues overleaf

DECEMBER

21   MONDAY

22   TUESDAY

SHORTEST DAY

23   WEDNESDAY

24   THURSDAY

25   FRIDAY

CHRISTMAS DAY

26   SATURDAY

BOXING DAY / ST. STEPHEN'S DAY (REPUBLIC OF IRELAND)

27   SUNDAY

TRIPLE CHOCOLATE LOG
RECIPE

7 To make the white mousse, whip the cream with the vanilla until it thickens and stands in stiff peaks. Fold in the chocolate. Cover and keep in the fridge until needed.

8 To assemble the log, make a deep cut across the sponge about 1.5cm away from one short end. Spread the dark chocolate mousse over the sponge, leaving a 2cm border clear all around. Cover the dark mousse with the white mousse.

9 Roll up from the short end with the cut, using the baking paper to help you pull and mould the roll into a neat shape. Wrap the roll in the paper to give it a neat shape, then chill for at least 2 hours until firm (or up to a day if the roll is well covered).

10 When ready to finish, remove the paper and transfer the log to a serving platter. Trim off the ends, if you like. Temper the chocolate, then use to make leaves. Brush half of them with edible gold lustre. Leave to set.

11 Arrange the chocolate leaves down the length of the cake, then sprinkle with sifted cocoa powder. Any leftover cake can be kept in an airtight container in the fridge for up to 3 days.

TIP
Spoon the tempered dark chocolate into a disposable piping bag, snip off the tip and pipe 'Buche de Noel' on a strip of acetate or perspex. Leave to set before peeling from the acetate and placing gently on the cake.

DEC 2015/JAN 2016

28 MONDAY

BOXING DAY HOLIDAY / ST. STEPHEN'S DAY HOLIDAY (REPUBLIC OF IRELAND)

29 TUESDAY

30 WEDNESDAY

31 THURSDAY

1 FRIDAY

2 SATURDAY

3 SUNDAY

NOTES

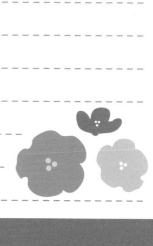

NOTES

NOTES

NOTES

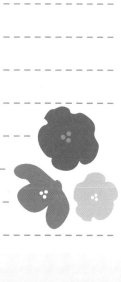

HOW TO MAKE

PRALINE

Praline is simply caramelized nuts. Once cold it can be broken into chunks for a decoration; chopped or crushed; or ground (in a food-processor) to a fine powder and added to butter icing, buttercream, ganache, whipped cream or ice cream.

Makes 200g

100g caster sugar

100g whole blanched almonds or hazelnuts, or a combination

Put the sugar and nuts into a medium-sized heavy-based pan and set over fairly low heat. Stir occasionally with a metal spoon until the sugar starts to melt. When all the sugar has melted turn up the heat to medium and cook until the mixture starts to colour, then stir gently until it turns a good chestnut-brown colour. Immediately pour onto a well-oiled baking sheet and leave to cool and set. Break up into chunks and store in a screw-topped jar for up to a month.

TIP

For a stronger flavour use unblanched nuts – that is, those with their papery brown skins still on.

CRÈME PÂTISSIÈRE

Also known as pastry cream, this thick and rich sweet vanilla egg custard mixture is used to fill all manner of desserts and pastries. Cornflour prevents the cooked egg mixture from separating and gives a velvety-smooth finish, and whipped cream adds lightness.

Flavour is added with vanilla extract, but you could substitute finely grated lemon or orange zest and/or a dash of fruit liqueur, or replace some of the milk with strong coffee to taste.

Makes about 500ml

250ml creamy milk

1 vanilla pod, split open OR finely grated zest of 1 medium unwaxed orange or lemon and/or 1 teaspoon liqueur (or to taste)

3 large free-range egg yolks, at room temperature

50g caster sugar

1½ tablespoons cornflour

150ml double or whipping cream, well chilled

1 Heat the milk with the split vanilla pod, or the zest, in a medium pan. Remove from the heat and leave to infuse for 10 minutes. If using a vanilla pod remove it and use the tip of a knife to scrape a few seeds out of the pod back into the milk (the pod can be rinsed, dried and used again or used to make vanilla sugar).

2 Set a heatproof bowl on a damp cloth (to stop it wobbling), add the egg yolks, sugar and cornflour and whisk for a couple of minutes until smooth, light and thick. Whisk in the hot milk, then tip the whole lot back into the pan. Set over medium heat and whisk constantly until the mixture boils and thickens to make a smooth custard – take care the mixture doesn't scorch on the base of the pan. Transfer to a clean bowl and press a piece of clingfilm or dampened greaseproof paper onto the surface to prevent a skin from forming. Cool, then chill thoroughly.

3 Whip the cream until it holds a soft peak. Stir the custard until smooth and stir in the liqueur, if using. Fold in the whipped cream. Use the crème pâtissière immediately or cover tightly and keep chilled for up to 4 hours.

PÂTE BRISÉE

1 Sift the flour and salt onto a clean worktop and make a large well in the centre. Put the butter between sheets of clingfilm and pound with a rolling pin until it is very supple but still cold. Cut the butter into pieces and put into the well with the egg yolk, sugar and water.

2 Put the fingertips of one of your hands together to form a beak shape and use to mash together the ingredients in the well. When they are thoroughly combined gradually work in the flour with your fingers, using a plastic dough scraper (or metal spatula) to help you draw the flour in. When the mixture looks like coarse crumbs, gather the whole lot together to make a ball of dough. If there are dry crumbs and the dough won't come together add more water a teaspoon at a time; if the dough is really sticky work in a little more flour.

3 Lightly dust the worktop with flour and start to gently work the dough: press down on the ball of dough with the heel of your hand and push it away from you, then gather up the dough into a ball once more (using the scraper) and

repeat. Continue working for a couple of minutes – no more – until the dough is silky-smooth and very pliable, so pliable it can be pulled off the worktop in one piece. Shape into a ball, then flatten to a thick disc. Wrap tightly in clingfilm and chill for 30 minutes before using.

CHOUX DOUGH

100g plain flour

¼ teaspoon salt

75g unsalted butter, diced

3 large free-range eggs, at room temperature, beaten

1 Sift the flour onto a sheet of greaseproof paper and set aside until needed. Put the salt, butter and 175ml water in a medium sized pan and heat gently until the butter has completely melted – don't let the water boil and begin to evaporate. Quickly bring the mixture to the boil, then tip in the flour all in one go.

2 Take the pan off the heat and beat furiously with a wooden spoon – the mixture will look a hopeless, gluey, lumpy mess at first, but as you beat it will turn into a smooth, heavy dough. Put the pan back on low heat and beat at a more gentle speed for a couple of minutes to slightly cook the dough until it will come away from the sides of the pan to make a smooth, glossy ball.

HOW TO MAKE

CHANTILLY CREAM

This sweetened whipped cream can be piped as a decoration or filling or served piled in a bowl. For the best results chill both your mixing bowl and whisk beforehand.

Makes about 350g

250ml whipping cream, very well chilled

2 tablespoons icing sugar, sifted

1 teaspoon vanilla extract

Whip the cream with the sugar and vanilla until just stiff enough to hold a peak. Use immediately or cover tightly and chill for up to an hour.

ROYAL ICING

This bright white icing, made from icing sugar and egg whites, is used to cover celebration cakes and for decoration. It can be piped or used for 'flooding' and run-outs as well as spreading. When using to cover a cake, mix in ½ teaspoon glycerine: the icing will set firm but not rock-hard.

Makes enough to cover a 20.5cm round deep cake

2–3 large, very fresh free-range egg whites, at room temperature

Few drops of lemon juice

½ teaspoon glycerine (optional – see above)

500–600g icing sugar, sifted

1 Put 2 of the egg whites, the lemon juice and glycerine, if using, in a large bowl and beat with a wooden spoon until thoroughly combined. Gradually beat in the icing sugar to make an icing that is completely smooth. For coating and piping, the icing should be fairly thick and leave a solid trail. Icing for run-outs and flooding should be slightly softer, so beat in the extra egg white a tablespoon at a time until you have a consistency that is pourable but still thick enough to coat the back of the spoon. (The icing must be free of air bubbles, which could ruin the final appearance. If your icing does have a lot of bubbles simply press a piece of clingfilm onto the surface and leave at room temperature overnight.)

2 Use immediately, or press clingfilm onto the surface of the icing, tightly cover the bowl and keep in the fridge for up to a week.

3 Royal Icing can be coloured or tinted using edible food colouring, which is available in many colours and even shimmery tones. Add a tiny amount of colouring using a cocktail stick and mix in well before adding more – some colours darken as they set. If you are trying to match a colour scheme, always do a trial on a small cake or biscuit first.

NOTE

If you are avoiding eating raw eggs you can make the icing using ready-made Royal Icing sugar.